DISNEY · PIXAR

BRAVE

Adapted by
Alexandra West

Illustrated by the
Disney Storybook Art Team

First Boxed Set Edition, August 2017
5 7 9 10 8 6 4
ISBN 978-1-368-00657-6
FAC-025393-20061
Printed in China
For more Disney Press fun, visit www.disneybooks.com

This is Merida.
She lives in a castle.
She is a princess.

Merida has three brothers.
They are triplets.
They love to eat treats.
They love to cause trouble.

Merida's mother is
Queen Elinor.
Her father is
King Fergus.

The queen thinks it is time
for Merida to get married.

Merida is mad.
She does not want to get married.

Lords from the other clans
come to the castle.
Each brings his
oldest son.

One young lord from each
clan will compete.
The winner will get
to marry Merida.

Merida gets to
choose the event.
The young lords must shoot
an arrow at a target.

The young lords shoot.
Merida walks onto the field.
She shoots, too.
She wins the game.

The queen is mad.
Merida did not act
like a princess.

Merida is mad.
She tears a family picture
with her sword.

Merida runs away.
She goes to the woods.
She sees a cottage.
A witch is inside.

Merida asks the witch for
a spell to change her mum.
The witch gives her
a magic cake.

Merida goes home.
She gives the cake
to her mum.

The queen eats the cake.
The queen feels sick.
She turns into a bear!

Merida and her mum need
to break the spell.
They go to the cottage.
The witch is gone!

There is a
message for Merida:
"Mend the bond
torn by pride."

Merida does not know
what to do.
She and her mum
spend the day together.

For the first time
in a long time,
they have fun.

Merida and her mum find
an old castle.
There is a broken stone inside.
The stone shows four brothers.

Now Merida knows
what to do.
She must fix the
picture she tore.

Merida and her mum go
back to the castle.
Merida's brothers ate the cake.
Now they are bears, too!

The clans see the queen.
They think she is a real bear!
They chase her
into the woods.

Merida and her brothers
have to save their mum!
The boys steer Merida's horse.
She fixes the picture she tore.

The king draws his sword.
He does not know that
the bear is the queen!

Merida steps in front
of the king.
She tells him the truth.

Merida covers her mum
with the picture.
She starts to cry.

Merida is sorry.
She tells her mum
she loves her.

Love breaks the spell!
The queen changes back.
Merida's family is whole again.